THIS BLOOMSBURY BOOK

BELONGS TO

....

For Philippa Milnes-Smith — M.B.

Bloomsbury Publishing, London, Berlin, New York and Sydney

First published in Great Britain in March 2012 by Bloomsbury Publishing Plc
50 Bedford Square, London, WC1B 3DP

Text copyright © Mara Bergman 2012
Illustrations copyright © Emily Bolam 2012

The moral rights of the author and illustrator have been asserted

Manufactured and supplied under licence from the Zoological Society of London

A CIP catalogue record for this book is available from the British Library

ISBN 978 1 4088 1847 3

FSC
www.fsc.org

MIX
Paper from
responsible sources
FSC® C104723

Printed in China by Toppan Leefung Printing Ltd, Dongguan, Guangdong

1 3 5 7 9 10 8 6 4 2

www.bloomsbury.com

www.storiesfromthezoo.com

The Zoological Society of London (ZSL) is a charity that provides help for animals at
home and worldwide. We also run ZSL London Zoo and ZSL Whipsnade Zoo.

By buying this book, you have helped us raise money to continue our work
with animals around the world.

Find out more at **zsl.org**

ZSL
LIVING CONSERVATION

ZSL
LONDON
ZOO

ZSL
WHIPSNADE
ZOO

Itchy Itch Itch

Mara Bergman

Illustrated by Emily Bolam

BLOOMSBURY

LONDON BERLIN NEW YORK SYDNEY

In a land where it's hot and where coconuts grow,
all the animals were grazing, except Buffalo.

Buffalo had an itchy itch itch,
which he couldn't quite reach to
scratchy scritch scritch!

Buffalo said, 'Whatever shall I do?'
Buffalo thought until Buffalo knew.

Elephant was big and strong
with ears that flapped
and a trunk that was long.

Buffalo said, 'Would you kindly scratch my back?
I have an **itchy itch** and I can't reach it to scratch!'

'ABSOLUTELY!' Elephant said,

and she scratched

and scratched

and scratched.

But Buffalo's fur was too shaggy and thick
and Buffalo **still** had that itchy **itch itch.**

Buffalo said, 'Whatever shall I do?'
Buffalo thought until Buffalo knew.

Monkey was small but Monkey was strong
and Monkey had arms that were really quite long.

Buffalo said, 'Would you kindly scratch my back?
I have an **itchy itch** and I can't reach it to scratch!'

'It would be my PLEASURE!' Monkey said,

and he scratched

and scratched

and scratched.

But Buffalo's fur was too shaggy and thick
and Buffalo STILL had that itchy itch itch.

Buffalo said, 'Whatever shall I do?'
Buffalo thought . . . but he hadn't a clue.

Bird wasn't big and Bird wasn't strong
and she didn't have arms that were bendy and long.

But her beady eyes were bright and her hungry beak snapped
at the itchy itch itches on Buffalo's back.

'Oh, Buffalo,' Bird sang, 'don't you see
that you and I were meant to be?

Though your fur may be shaggy and thick,
I can get rid of your itchy itch itch!'

And she pecked and picked
and picked and pecked . . .
till not a single itchy **itch itch** was left.

'Oh, Bird,' said Buffalo, 'won't you stay with me?
Together we can live happily.'

Bird replied, 'WHY, CERTAINLY!
To spend my days on your back
would suit me perfectly!'

In a land where it's hot and where coconuts grow,
all the animals were grazing, even Buffalo.

Now Buffalo never has an
itchy itch itch
that Bird can't reach to

scratchy
        scritch
scritch.

And Bird never has a rumbly tum
because Buffalo's **itchy itches** are so

yummy
yum
yum!

And they lived
together
happily for ever.
Scritch!

FUN ANIMAL Facts

Animals like the ones in this story live in Africa and Asia. Here are a few fun facts about each of them.

Buffaloes spend much of their day wallowing in muddy water. This helps them to keep annoying insects away! Their wide, hoofed feet help them to walk in the mud. They like to feed on grass and herbs. Both males and females have horns that curl backwards, but the males' horns are bigger.

Buffalo

Bird

Some birds perch on the backs of buffaloes to feed on the insects that live on their hides. Buffaloes let these birds sit on their backs because they pick off pests and ticks. (And scratch their itches!) The birds also call out a warning when predators, such as lions, come near — helping the buffaloes to keep safe!

The elephant is the largest animal that lives on land. An elephant's trunk is more than just a nose! It is like an extra hand it uses for doing lots of things. It can reach up high for food, suck up water, tear down trees, even pick berries. Elephants eat grass, leaves, twigs, bark, fruit and seeds.

Elephant

Monkey

Monkeys are very clever animals. They use sticks to collect insects to eat and use leaves to scoop up water to drink. They spend hours every day grooming each other — searching one another's hair and skin to pick off the bugs and eat them. They even pull faces — just like us!